PARAGRAPH 175

Matthew Noel

Dedicated to:

The silenced voices of the Shoah

And to Alice Goldstein whose personal experiences
and insight helped make this story possible

INTRODUCTION: THE AFTERLIFE

What is it like to be reborn?

The silence is deafening
                    I float above deep pools
Awareness
Soul detaches
Flood of emotions
Feel earth's pulse vibrating
Me its heartbeat
Abstract
complex
being
Ignorant of own capabilities
Until now

Wind of knowledge lifts me
high above human limitations

Below
the world appears
microscopic

Who am I?
Phantom caught between faded lines
                            History pages omit me
Country erased all traces

Universe unshackles silenced voice
Army of ghosts wait
Strangled voices cry up from the soot

Memory eludes
I try to write on skin
Tattooed numbers create lifelines

PART I:

Son of the Fatherland

1: BIRTH

Quaint German village
I am born
Dieter Bastian Khun
Cradled by vast mountains
Soft face
Inquisitive eyes
Searching the air
Gulping first breaths
Cough up afterbirth
Twilight kisses
clenched fingers
Future shields her horrors
My little Dieter
Mama's auburn wisps tickle my nose
I am you and you are me
He will be strong
Papa's peppered mustache curls
Son of the Fatherland
Son of poverty
of black dirt
The forgotten
We will rise up
from the ashes
Papa coos until
wide bright eyes
flutter shut
Fast asleep

2: BLUE DISHES

Childhood home
Farmhouse
pulled from
storybook pages
Plain wood shutters
Stone gray plastered siding
Smooth oak bannisters against
narrow lavender walls
Backdoor opens
Endless green fields
Sea of waving grass
Sanctuary from reality
I hide behind rainbows
Gorge on simplicity

Mama's cherished baby blue dishes
Stored safely in rustic antique cabinets
Gift given by Oma Elke
after the war
Most prized possessions

Dieter
heirlooms are important
because they remind us of where
we come from

Mama
I am cracked porcelain
Thieves stole my identity
piece
by
piece
Danced on mortal body

Matthew Noel

Broken
against the rocks

3: COCOON

The trees speak to me
Gentle hands
tenderly caress
gnarled bark
Moss cushions path
beneath bare feet
Rushing water
baptizes innocence
Creation unfolds
Given breath
Meant to exist
As I am
Dieter? Where are you?
Mama's panicked voice
I enjoy running
away from home
Five years old
Climbing walls
Crowns of primrose
Childhood cocoon
Rest your weary head
Mama chants
Safe at last

4: THE KING AND I

> Six years old
> Prince of the field
> Carve whistle
> out of willow branch
> Favorite pasttime
> I feel like a king

> Fierce little bird
> lies on the ground
> Left green wing hangs
> Soft hands encase fragility
> Gangly legs run home shouting

Mama! Come Quick!

What is it child?
Head hangs out window
Face smudged with flour

This bird is hurt

> Frightened creature pants
> Nervous flapping subsides
> Fingers stroke its orange
> and yellow head crest
> White chest heaves

Looks like a broken wing
Mama nurtures bird
Long oak table
Operation room

Is it going to die?

He will be alright
Constructs sling
Tiny branches
Strip of cloth
In our stories

the Goldcrest
is known as
King of the Birds
Nobility
You did a kind thing
Because of you he will live
Mama washes hands
Pinches my cheek affectionately

                    Can he stay with us?

Only until he can fly again

        Bow head
        Solemn
    Curtsey to bird

What are you doing?
Mama holds back laughter

               He's royalty!

My sweet boy
Butterfly kiss to the forehead

5: TOY TRAINS I

Seven
years
old
Festive
Christmas
market

Wait my
little prince!

Papa chases
I ignore him
Divulging
childish
impulses
feet pound
cobblestoned
streets
Villagers
stroll
admiring
homemade trinkets
on display
Carved manger scenes
Handcrafted toys
Elaborate wreaths
Nose
tingles
Smells
waft
Roasted
chestnuts
imported
from

Italy
Hints of
clove
Chocolate
covered
marzipan
Eyes feast
Mouth waters

Always in
a rush

Papa
chuckles
tussling
my raven hair
Can I have
a toy train?
Please?
Desperate plea
Hardly able
to contain
excitement

I'm sorry
but not
this year

Wisps
of defeat
cast
shadows
over
Papa's
sun wrinkled
face

6: TOY TRAINS II

Hand on my shoulder

Face lights up
Awestruck
Wooden toy train
Polished
Exquisite
Papa says we can't afford it
Blames the War
Treaty
of
Versailles
fucked us over
Took
our
land
Pounded us
into the
ground
Made us pay
Papa works
bone-spent hours
raising hearty beef cattle
Ploughing dried up fields
Palms calloused
Body worn down
Faith in Germany
undaunted
Don't worry son
Germany will find
her way again
and we will be

on top
once more!
Then you
can have
any toy train
your heart
desires!

7: BOYS

Bored
Mr. Muller's
mathematics class
Pass the time
daydreaming
Otto Van Hoffman's
honey locks
Shape of his neck

Recess

Straighten
new button up
navy shirt
I strut
past

tripping

oversized
shoes

Luckily
he doesn't
witness
my
embarrassing

fall

8: OTTO

Last month of summer's humidity
He invites me
to come help
on the farm
Ecstatic
I rake hay
Tend to animals
Chop firewood
We eat our lunches
by gurgling creek
Evening sun
burns down
Water's edge
Back against sturdy oak
Otto beside me
Mesmerized
Inches apart
Ragged
breath
against
my
face
I think
my
heart
might
burst
Thump
Thump
Thump
Lips
graze

Tinges
of
dirt
Tilled
earth
Savor
taste
Guilt
pulls
him
away
Confusion
hangs
in sweltering air
I
regret
nothing
Body
craves
more
I'm sorry Dieter
I shouldn't have done that
Words
like
bullets
to my chest
Water
washes
away
rejection

9: REVELATIONS

School
New year
Pass Otto leaving
Geography Class
Eyes
cast
down
Kiss never happened
He
looks
right

           through
          me

                Invisible

He drools over
Nina Ziegler a senior
I hate how she twirls
slender fingers
around curly locks
Despise the way his eyes pop out
Flirtatious antics
Bat
   of
an
   eyelash
Silent command

           Hallway during lunch period
                He kisses her
                 in front of me
       Twelve-year old heart splinters
              Restless sleep
                Dreams

Matthew Noel

I taste his breath
Born different
Otto my first

10: MANHOOD

              Thirteen years old Summer rain pelts down
                         Lucy
                      Family cat
                       Calico
          Left eye blue   Right eye brown
                     Seeks shelter
                    Musty dry barn
Hayloft
Scratchy straw
Chirping barn swallows
Chapel
Nose deep in a book
Come here boy!
Papa calls
Shiver
Run
Bare feet
Show the boys what you can do!
Papa's friends from the valley
Tobacco farmers
Rough around the edges
Eyes scrutinize
Sniffing out weakness

Freshly cut wood pile
Oak logs bigger than me
Stacked
Scrawny arms
Soft hands
Wrap around biggest log
Impossible

Foolish mistake
Heave
Tug
Adrenaline rush
Papa Friends
shout encouragement
Do it son!
Be a man!
                    Maybe I will become a man today
Weight
Overbearing
Knees sink
Gooey mud
Crushed
underneath
Get up!
Bark scrapes skin
Get up queer!
Papa vomits bullets
Friends'
laughter
                        bounces
off soggy ground
Iron soldier
Papa curses
Scramble to my feet
There's not a boy
in this village
who couldn't lift that
Papa cuts
Cringe
You embarrass me
Stormy eyes
                        I'll never be
                        what you hope for

You're a wimp

Pathetic piece of shit
Words
Sharp
Precise
Slash
Feet have a mind of their own
Fight or flight
                    Always flight

Face against the wind
I hide in the forest
Behind charcoal black barn
Stifled sobs
Papa does not come after me
He's occupied mulling
over his disappointment

11: THE SCENT OF WOLVES

Election
Day

         Red
         white
         black
         bleed
         onto
         streets

Democracy
dissipates
Intimidation
billows
over
heads
Nazi
enthusiasts
make
presence
known
Prowl
outside
voting
booths
Vote Nazi!
Hitler will
make Germany
great again!
Hitler will bring
back jobs!
Hitler stands
with the
working class!

Honey
coated
lies
ooze
out
of
their
mouths
Proudly
display
Swastika
pins
Party
over
country
It only takes
one
single
vote
Radio
announcer's
voice
crackles
Adolf Hitler
is
New
Chancellor
of Germany
Mama
prays
quietly
Papa
pours
foaming
beer
Beams

Matthew Noel

from
ear
to
ear

12: DEAR FELLOW CITIZENS

The antichrist rang the doorbell today with lies on his tongue
whispering rumors of wars
Delivered letters hidden in red envelopes stuffed down my
throat

I tied white ribbons to the trees
Sign of the end times

Everyone is deaf

Wave your flags for all to see your delusional patriotism
Cover your head with ashes
The tin men are marching home
array of silver hands gliding over statues dissolving
Replace country with twisted crosses
March like blind beggars
Taunt bleeding hearts

Bring out the welcome wagon
See your broken pawns strewn
Mere trinkets of the grand scheme
Parade
Flaunt
Show the world your towers of ivory built on quick sand
Lick the wounds you punctured
Taste what is left of your burning democracy

Sincerely,

Dieter

13: FALSE PROPHET

Mass
Sunday
morning
Mama insists
Papa put on
his best suit
hat and tie
Worn
prayer
book
Wood
rosary
I straighten
my shirt
before entering
St. Ann's
Fr. Ulrich
family
priest
Thickset
Bald head
Flushed cheeks
Blusters
Blows   out
hot steam

Our country has been
invaded by cunning
tricksters
The Jews
Christ killers
Kidnappers of German dignity!
Adolf Hitler is a servant of God

It is up to us as God fearing christians
to assist him in his mission

Papa nods
his head
in agreement
Echoes

Amen

Mama
fidgets
nervously
on the hard
wooden pew
overlapping
gloved hands
I want
to leave
Papa's eyes
forbid it
I cringe
Mama
intercedes

Hail Mary,
full of grace...

14: MOTHER MARY

After Mass I wait basking before your hardened stone face
Eyes
shed
concrete
tears
Knees
burn
Your wandering son crawls in the dirt begging
Mother of outcasts break the stained glass before bombs eradi-
cate what glistens inside of me

15: SIXTEEN

A:

Where are you off to boy?
Papa's face deep
in the Völkischer Beobachter
The People's Observer
Newspaper sent by Uncle Herman from Berlin

Leave him alone Klein
It's his birthday after all
Brave Mama

Otto is hosting a bonfire at his house
Avoid further questioning
Check reflection
Smudged hall mirror
Chiseled chin
Stubborn stubble
Damn
Need to sharpen
my razor
Cropped hair
slicked back
Red stripes
Short sleeves
Dapper
Take your sweater
The mountains cast a shadow
in the evenings
Mama always worries
I won't be out too late
Kiss forehead
Out the door

Freedom
Otto's family's farm
few miles away
Drink in solitude
Pink wisps paint sailor's sky
And I am sixteen years old
Evening chill wraps around me
Grateful for blue sweater
stitched by Mama's gentle hands
Why do I want to cry?
Childhood eludes me
I don't know who I am
I was older years ago

B:
Wandering pilgrim
Locked in a shell
Tossed between the tide
True self overshadowed
Farmer's tan
Vines reach out
Barbed wire
Face in the mirror
Lines drawn
Reflection hidden
Busted fists against
lavender walls
Dried blood
One day in wonderland
blurs into years
Men drenched
Rough course lips brushing
Thoughts
Fantasies
Painful to be alive
To Exist
Self hatred attacks

Humiliation cuts
Wise voice speaks
Smash the poison
Power courses
Hope trumpets
Stronger than the demons
that chase me
Human
Homosexual
Composed of cosmic light
Flesh and bones
Twisted up
Fabric of emotions
Beautiful goldenrod

16: BONFIRE

Dieter! You made it!
Otto's arms flail
Drunk

Did you break into
your Pop's wine?
Push him away playfully

Lighten up
Tonight is a celebration!
Look at you! How'd you afford a fancy shirt?
Teases
The better question is
why are you
dressed like that?

I joined the Hitler Youth
Pop says we all have to do
our part for the Fatherland
Awkward
Let's go join the others
Wary of his lingering touch
Hand on my arm
I drift through the group
Wood piled high
Everyone is here
even that new kid from Berlin
Gunther Heisenberg
Otto follows closely
Out of breath

Short legs
New military boots weigh him down
Small price to pay for selling his soul

Search the crowd
Hungry for a new face
All the familiar sketches smile back at me
Schoolmates barely know I exist
Eyes dance towards unfamiliar face
He peers at me from behind
wide rimmed glasses
Want to read his body
Trace cheek bones
Follow every path
that leads me to my knees

Someone lights the kindling
Flames engulf
Heat glares
Smoke chokes air

Stranger makes his way next to me

Exhale

It is a nice evening for a bonfire

Yes it is
What comes next?
Panic
Don't panic

Breathe in
and out

I'm Dieter
Are you new to the village?
Gunther
Yes I moved here a few days ago

Matthew Noel

with Mutter and Vater

Abashedly wrings hands
I've lived here my whole life

It's nice to have
somewhere to call home
He smiles
Bare arms
Carpet of dark hair

I fall off the edge
God promise me forgiveness
He chuckles at my quirkiness
I feed off of his shameless charm

Summer wind
Boyhood floats   Levitating
Touch my eyes so I remember

The hours tick by
Time SCREAMS at us
Warns us
Our lives are not ours to enjoy
Cross the barbed wire Haunt my nightmares

March through my heart Settle within my palm

Delicate

17: THE WALK

Charred mouths   Rich sweet wine
Phonograph blares cabaret music   Sweaty bodys sway
Lonely night sky eats cinders

Otto ignores me
Dances enraptured by Willem   Dutch boy from school
Alcohol makes him bold

        He should be more careful
        Nazi eyes are everywhere

Would you like some company on your way home?
Gunther draws me back in

       We should all be more careful

I would like that very much
Red heat rushes to cheeks
Sheepish smile
We walk side by side
Words tumble out
Jumbled sentences

            Do you enjoy living here?
I   break   *the   si-*
lence   *It is quiet*
unlike the city

        More time to think
        In Berlin we had a library
        right down the street
        It was my favorite pastime
        He blooms

Matthew Noel

I catch a glimpse
Books are a luxury around here

Is there no library?
Disappointment
Desperation

No unfortunately there isn't

Knowledge is important
Dark eyebrows narrow
We can write our own stories

Solution brings enthusiastic smile
I like that idea
Voice cracks
Dawn greets us

18: MIDNIGHT CONVERSATIONS

Why did you leave the city?

My parents thought it best

I've never been anywhere but here

Ah you would love Berlin!
The bright lights
The music!

His excitement
Infectious
It must be wonderful

We should visit sometime
Olive branch

I would like that
Jump head first

Tell me more about you,
No one has ever asked that.

There's not much to know
Pockets hide hands
Shy

What do you do
with your time?

Swim in the creeks
Bonfires
Reading
Chores

I'm sure we can find
new things to do
Mischievous grin
Coy

Glimmer of hope
Maybe he's like me!

Lamp glows from the porch up ahead

Well this is where I live

It's been a pleasure
walking with you
He bows

Stifle giggle
Amused
I've never met someone quite like you

That's a good thing I hope
Stars in his smile

It is I promise

Will you show me around the village tomorrow?

Yes I will be your tour guide

Danke schöen sir! I bid you gute nacht!
He twirls
Dramatic flare
Tenor voice sings

I am his choir

Trees swallow silhouette

Loneliness rears
its ugly head

19: BEFORE I KNEW ME

Maybe the sun will rise before I explode

Dirty sheet
Second time tonight

                                        3:00am
Heated dreams

Twilight collides
Early dawn drips
sticky wonders

I find you
Back turned
Draped in clarity
Lips parted
Inhale
Right hand grips
Pulsating
Exhale
Release
Only a kiss
Just one from you
Is that too much to ask?
Eye lids flutter open
Confronted by white ceiling
Four walls
My room

                                        Unfortunately

Could I be anywhere but here?
Fantasies keep me company
Trek across sand dunes
Throat parched
Mirage

Stand outside my door
Open it softly
Come Inside
Breathe

20: RUMORS

> *I am coming with you*
> *Mama straightens her hat*
> *not giving me a chance to protest*

How many times can she adjust that hat?
She only wears it on special occasions
Gift from Papa
to compensate for
his unpredictable rage
She wears it
Ribbons of black
Badge of honor

But Mrs. Heisenberg
isn't expecting you
I plead
Subtly try to
dissuade her

> *We must welcome them to the village*
> *Mama states matter of factly*
> *Appearance satisfactory*
> *She's made up her mind*

I follow her
reluctantly
out the door
Straw basket
crook of her arm
Wrapped safely inside
Linzertorte
Nutty
Raspberry
jam filled cake

Matthew Noel

Freshly baked
early this morning
Mama tries to heal
the world with food

I am supposed to show Gunther the village
Birds chirp excitedly
Sun warms the earth

Mama pauses
You should be careful

Why do you say that?

I've heard rumors about that boy
Mama lowers her eyes
Uncomfortable

What rumors?

Inappropriate things
She won't budge

Mama, you can't believe gossip

I heard it from a very respected friend
Adjusts her hat

Who? Ingrid Malzan?

That is Mrs. Malzan to you
Reprimanded
Still a little boy in her eyes

Mrs. Malzan spreads rumors

That may be but truth stems from rumors

*What is it that
she mentioned
about Gunther?*

It isn't polite to speak of such things
Just be cautious of him

I'm not a child anymore
you can speak truthfully with me

Jump over rain puddle

Mama sidesteps
He is a troubled boy
with unnatural desires

Desires?
Heart pounds
Ears ring

Enough Dieter
Mama is stubborn

We walk the rest of the way
cloaked in morning fog

21: LINZERTORTE

Mama hands me the basket
Tugs flower print dress
Knocks on door
Woman
Fiery red hair
Styled in
latest fashion
opens the door
Film star grace
She politely smiles
Long lashed eyes
try to hide
quick flash
of fear
Annoyance
Guttentag
how may I help you?

Guttentag
I am Heidi Kuhn and this is my son Dieter

Monika Heisenberg
Melodic voice

We are here to welcome you to the village
Mama offers her the linzertorte
She craves friendship

Mrs. Heisenberg softens
How thoughtful! Please come in
We step inside
Curious eyes scan
spacious living room
No sign of Gunther

Thank you for stopping by
We haven't had a chance to
get to know anyone here
Mrs. Heisenberg offers us seats
Cozy kitchen decorated in homemade art
Gunther said you would be stopping by
Mrs. Heisenberg
serves Mama's cake
Every movement a dance

I want to be like her
Elegant
Sophisticated

How are you adjusting?
Mama treads lightly
Uneasy making conversation

My family is safe so I am happy
Mrs. Heisenberg dodges details

Family are all that matters
Mama agrees

Both women share a gaze
Unspoken acknowledgment

Village life can be hard but we look out for each other
Mama extends compassion
Mrs. Heisenberg accepts

22: SUITS

Cloves and cinnamon on my breath

Dieter
are you
ready to go?
Gunther shouts from outside

Mama gives me the go ahead despite apprehensions

You boys have fun
Mrs. Heisenberg sings

Gunther
Blue and white striped suit
Tie
Hat perched on coal black locks
He smiles
It is good to see you
Blushing
I dip my head
Embarrassed by worn trousers
Torn burgundy shirt
Mama says suits are for church not hiking

What part of the village would you like to see first?

Wherever you want to take me
I'm all yours

We
walk
shoulders
brushing
Hands
ache

23: PRIVATE KINGDOM

Did you have many friends in Berlin?

A few but one in particular

Do you miss them?

No I do not
Secrets float
around him

The Inns are lined along the path
Change topic
hoping to distract him

Let's go!
He runs ahead
like a kid
released from
confines of school
Villagers wave
I nod in greeting
Rumors are buzzing
about the new boy
in town

Dieter come on!
Gunther urges
Sunlight adorns
princely head

Village left behind
I forget
who I am
Legs stretch out
Ancient trees bend

Reverence

24: MOUNTAINS

Heavy branches laden with juicy red apples
Vater spends his time in the city mostly on business
But Mutter prefers the quiet village life
It calms her nerves

Your mother seems very kind

She is
I'm lucky

                              Violets
                              tickle
                              our toes

I prefer
the grass
against
my skin
Gunther says

            Past the Inns we follow the trail up a grassy knoll
Choppy
river
cuts
through
mountains
Warm wind
pulls at our sleeves

Dieter you are the luckiest fellow in the world
Look at this view!
I never saw sights like this in the city
His
arm
thrown

Matthew Noel

casually over
my sun burned shoulder
Sweaty skin sticks
Savor salt

25: KISSING FROGS

Wide open skies above us

Rushing river
below
us

Have you ever been kissed?
Gunther asks slyly

Once
a long
time ago

What was her name?

I pause
Reluctant
His name
was Otto

Gunther's
smile
reassures

We are kindred spirits

What do
you mean?
Pulse quickens
Clammy hands

I like to kiss boys too
Do you like boys
the way you're supposed
to like girls?

Freezing cold
Shaking
Sometimes
I'm so afraid

Matthew Noel

of who I
think I am
Gunther
Sensitive
touch
Fingertips trail
across
quivering veins

I know how lonely it can be having
no
one
to confide in about these things

His
hand
on
mine
doesn't
feel
unnatural
It's what
I've been
yearning for
Courage
swells
Yes
I like
boys

26: PAPER

No one understands
what it's like to vanish

Wrap yourself around me
until I disappear

The wind carries my remains

Rickety skeletal frame stands alone

Forgotten
Isolated by laws
I went against nature
to find you

Empty pages wiped clean cry out for a story

History writes the remainder with invisible ink and I evaporate

Your pulse beats
against mine

Your hands are water
flowing over my chest
Freak of genetics
Winding downstream
I catch glimpses of sunlight
through whispering bare branches

The trees are our witnesses
We write our lifelines on their paper
Leaves
red yellow brown burn
before our bodies
turn to snow

27: SHELTER ME

Vengeful storm clouds
Angels cry

                    God must
                    be angry

Let's go over there
Gunther
points
Grove
Beech
trees
shelter
Quiet
solitude
Gentle raindrops
Damp hair
Clothes cling
Shy rabbits dance
across wheat fields
Lone fox leaps
Shakes apricot fur

Gunther guards
my secret
Armor
Faithful
Knight

                              Can I kiss you?
                              Bold words

Poised anticipation
Lean closer
Grasp blindly
Catch rainbows

Subtle ecstasy

Why does it feel as if
I've always known you?
He whispers
Lips nibble ear

Vernal heart   soars

28: IF WALLS COULD TALK

Midday sun scorches necks

I hope I didn't make you uncomfortable

No not at all
Thank you
for letting me
confide in you
Reassurance confirmed

Gunther glows
Then I can see you again?

I would like that
Fate sealed

Enter apartment
Walls close in
Dieter, your mother left
to prepare dinner
She said for you
to come home
Mrs. Heisenberg
smiles kindly
offers lemonade
Pulls
Gunther
aside
away
from
earshot

Tiptoe Eavesdrop Cracked door

I hope you know
what you are doing

Mrs. Heisenberg
Motherly concern

Mutter I will be careful
Confidence ignores truth

Remember
people here are
small minded
It isn't their fault
Village life is all
they've ever known

Yes
I am
aware of that
Eye roll

Just please be cautious
We can't afford to move again
And it isn't safe
with these Nazis
running about
Dieter isn't like the others

That's what you said about Ingo
and look how that turned out
Fresh wound punctured
Voice
falters
Please
don't
bring
Ingo
into
this

Mrs. Heisenberg
Apologetic

Protective hand
cradles stubbled cheek
Embrace

I love you
Mutter

Forgiven

29: PATRIOTISM

Early evening
Heisenberg's apartment
Papa shuffles playing cards

Mr. Heisenberg
Amber eyes
Smooth oval face
*We appreciate
you taking Gunther
under your wing*

Papa humphs
Flushed cheeks
Three beers tipsy
*Boys their age
should be working
Doing chores
Joining the Hitlerjugend
Build character and skills*

*Ah but intelligent conversation
helps the mind develop
Nature heals the soul*
Mr. Heisenberg
interjects

Papa scoffs
*All young boys
should be doing
their part for
the Fatherland*

Mr. Heisenberg
chooses words carefully
*I admire patriotism
but when the love*

Matthew Noel

for one's country
comes with the
exclusion
of others
I must firmly
disagree

Juden have
always been a
problem
Foreigners
taking up housing
Stealing jobs
Hitler will
rid us of them
It is what's best
for Germany
Papa sips on
certainty

30: WORLD ON FIRE

Gunther
tugs
arm
Leads
me outside
Summer
insects
hum
Adults only
ever argue
We should've
left Germany
while we still
had the chance
Guarded secrets
Wilts
Face
burrows into
my chest
Muffled whisper
Things are going to change

                    What do
                  you mean?

The
Nazis
won't
stop
until...
Panicked breaths
I saw them do
terrible things

Matthew Noel

in Berlin
Flames glare
Eyes burn
World
on fire

31: RACHEL'S TEARS

Crowded
market
Shopping
with Mama
Broken glass crunches
underneath shoes
Quiet street littered
Zealous Nazi soldiers
ransack
Jewish
shops
Jewish
homes

Complicit feet
step over
scattered
remnants

Enraged mob
thirsts for
sacrificial blood
Terrified screams
Helpless yellow stars
herded
into ominous vans
Fellow citizens
duck heads
Turn guilty eyes away
Complacent
Ordinary day
at the market

Somewhere
Rachel

Matthew Noel

weeps
for
her
children

32: EYES WIDE OPEN

Window pane
Pebble

      bounces

  Startled

                Bolt
             upright

Groggy

    Stumble

Gunther's
slim figure
Bright moon
casts shadows
Window raises
Afraid
Elated
*What are
you doing
here?*

I had to see you

Longing
warms
heart
Pull shirt
over head
Pull on pants
Tranquil
snores
Mama

and Papa
sound asleep
Free
No
more
words
Village
sleeps
We come to life
Let's go
to Berlin
Dancing eyes tempt

But you said
terrible things
are happening
there
Hesitant
Terrible things
are happening here!
They're rounding up
all of the Jews just like in Berlin
Wild
Uninhibited
Desperate
We should
see the city
one last time
before it
disappears

We can't leave

Words steal hope

Future
already

written

33: DEFIANCE

Let's disappear
Willing victim
Abducted
Transcending
I don't want
to hurt you
Body prepared
Adrenaline rush
Mouth parts
Succulent
Receive
Gasp
I trust you
Lips tease
Hips straddle
Fit perfectly
Defined chest
Angel wings
Halo
Oblivion
Ice blue stars explode
Black hole
Disappear
Tufts of hair
Curls
Rock
back
and
forth
                              Don't stop

Breathless plea
Fireflies burn

Defiance
of
a Nation

Reborn

34: AWAKE

Your
skin
paper
thin

stretches

across my heart

Chest
heaves

Treacherous
road

But
with
you
walls
tumble
Broken
parts
rebuild
Wounded soul
gasps
Oxygen
And
I
plunge

below

Exhilarated
Lifted up
View

from
your
shoulders
breathtaking

35: SLEEPING BEAUTY

Smell
of cows
Wood stoves crackle
Dawn teases
Papa will be furious
Mama worried

Time
slipped
away

Morning dew
coats wheat fields
Wool blanket
Stiff neck
Bare chest
Branches cover secrets
Youthful body
Sacrificial lamb
Altar adorned
Drenched
masculinity
Leftovers
Ravenous
Tingling sensation
Throbbing pulses
Hands reach
across barriers
Kaleidoscope
Bursts of color
written on skin
His
scent
Tip of my tongue

Soft rays stream through
cracked leaves
Interrupted
Reminder
We are human after all

36: ALIVE

Have you ever been standing
feet firmly planted on the ground
caught
between
who you
thought
you were
and who
you really
are?

Mysteriously
life seems to open up
and give you everything
you've ever wanted
Possibilities once unimaginable
bloom and grace your fingertips
It is like breathing for the first time
and you think:
This is it! This is what it means to be alive
With new found awareness,
you don't care how it happened or why
you only hope that your eyes
will stay open like this forever

37: THE WALK HOME

Morning breaks
Lighthearted
kick in my step
Nothing can bring me
down

Birds sing
Sleepy village comes to life
Colors seem more vibrant
than I remember
Gunfire

                          fades

War
ceases
Swastikas
go up in glorious flames
Someone
loves me
Turbulent world
beautiful place
once more

38: BREAKFAST

                                        Slip through the back door
Tiptoe

Careful

Avoid

creaks

Sizzling
sausages hiss
Cast iron skillet
Mama sweats
Stubborn ringlets
escape loose braid

                                        Dieter where
                                        have you been?

Concern
repressed
Racing mind
searches
can't come up
with a convincing lie

                                        If your Papa sees you...
                                        Unspoken fears exposed
                                        Quick
                                        get to your room
                                        He's still shaving

Ruffled apron shoos
                        Retreat behind
                        closed door
                        Grumbling stomach
                        feeds off of
                        last night's

aftertaste
Daydream
Starving
for more

39: RAINBOW

Colors
drip
Veins
open
I glide
through
shelves
Zombies
raid clique
Picket fences
Dream
sketched
Silhouette
against
white
canvas
You
A blur
Heavy eyes adjust
Skin
against
skin
Maybe
I'll
find
the truth
buried
beneath the rubble

40: SECRETS

Summer
evening
Ploughs
put away
Horses fed
Village boys run

                             Kick
                               up
                             dust

Silver
Creek
clothes off
Relaxed laughter
Rough housing
Dieter!
Gunther!
Otto
waves
head
above
Crystal clear water
Gunther
beside me
We should leave

                         It'll be okay

He strips
Water's edge
Wind tickles skin
Goosebumps
Heard you're a poof
Sneers
Threat

aimed
Gunther
freezes
Horst
fellow classmate
Nemesis
Ugly tan shirt
Black shorts
Swastika armband
I don't know what
you're talking about
Gunther
slips into
dry clothes
dripping
horror
Horst bares fangs

I heard you let a
man fuck you in
the ass
Then he reported
you

Straining ears
Prying eyes
Spotlight

Rush in
Protective arms steer Gunther to safety

Good leave!
You'd be best to stay away
We don't want your filth here

Death threat
Gunther
leans
close

Reserved
sobs

41: IN THE VALLEY OF THE SHADOWS

You should stay away from me
Gunther
Anxious
Frightened deer
Scent of predators
Rejects comfort
Alone
Soaking
Wise trees
Barricade
Sun kissed arms encircle
Sturdy fortress
Don't say that

Loving me isn't safe
I'll destroy you
Fights affection
Stubborn tears brim

Let me hold you
Grip
tightens
I won't let you go
Fragile frame encased
Body offered up
Sanctuary

I love him

42: INGO

This is
how it
happened
I will tell
you the
Truth
Gunther
releases

Musty
Crisp
Library
Shoulders
brushed
I commented
on his hat
Young
Easily fooled
He wanted
to kiss me
Ocean blue orbs
Charismatic
Invited
behind
trees
I lost
something
Mine to give

Elaborate promises
hushed whispers
I danced
Shimmering light

Alive

Precious hours
Fleeting minutes
Eyes
closed
Free
fall

Wealthy family
Arrogant
Afraid
Pressured
Prodded
Harassed
Ingo caved
Betrayal

Accusations
thrown
Stained
cobblestoned street
Gestapo forced me to say
I regretted him
That I was sorry

Imagine
apologizing for
breathing

Vater
Hero
bribed guards
Mutter
shielded my secret garden
Released
I escaped
to a life

without him
Prison

43: BABYLON

In the city that never sleeps dancing feet bleed
Babes drink milk from engines
Black tar clogs throats
Human ash coats freshly clipped lawns
Orphaned children play alongside ghosts
Dangers lurk   beside shadows
Greedy conquerers smear minorities
Enemies of the Fatherland
Brainwashed minds
worship propaganda
Self made prisons
Bare skin
Imprint
Rowing to and fro
Back and forth
Up and down
Forced laughter hides truth
Dragons pursuing stolen treasures consume yellow stars

Society rallies behind dictators
Midnight horses prance through rows of starving bald heads
Self professed gods smile wicked smiles
feeding an endless supply of ruin
Dreamers sleep in musty attics

                    waiting for liberation

                    to knock at their door

44: CHANGING FACES

Break from chores
Inside
Cool off
Mama?
No answer
Muffled noises
My bedroom
She sits
Dirty
floor
Papers
strewn
Hands
shaking
What is this?
What is happening to you?
Small wooden box
hidden underneath bed
Poems
Letters
Scribbles
Dedicated
to Gunther
Bite my lip
Why are you going
through my things?
Uncontrollable fury
Pounding heart
Mama
changes
Unrecognizable
I'm a stranger

invading her home

It's unnatural! That boy has corrupted you

Floor swallows me up

45: ASHES

Crumpled papers gathered
she leads me outside
Rusty barrel
Throw this
filth into the fire
before your Papa
comes home
Poems
slide
through
fingers
Words melt
Chest caves
Frustrated tears

I won't do it

Stunned
Mama
wrings
hands
snatches
papers
Lights
match
Darting
flame
Smoke
curls
I die

46: NATURE BOY

Runny nose
Blood shot eyes
Climb
Run
Gasp for breath

Need
him
next
to
me

Stubborn branches snag
Clothes rip

You may
not see
that
boy
ever
again
Mama's
words
replay
over
and
over
stinging

Pulse
races

Nowhere to hide

Arms
wrap
around
ancient oak

Heavy sobs
Mother Nature consoles

47: LAST DANCE

12:07am
Window pane
Crawl out of bed
Gunther's shadow outside
Desperate fingers tap

Head out the window
You shouldn't be here
Worried whisper

Why won't you talk to me?

I can't

Don't ignore me

I'm not

Then what's wrong?

Mama knows

Knows what?

About us
She said I can't see
you anymore

And you're just going to give in?

What other choice do I have?

We can't let them win!

They don't speak for God

Easy for you to say
You don't know
what it's like

Your parents
accept you

I want to be with you Dieter

Melt
Wobbly
knees
Sweaty foreheads
press together
Exhale
I love
you
Invite
him inside
Fall
asleep
Cheek
pressed
against
hairy
chest
Weary
heart
sighs

48: FREEDOM

Bedroom door creaks
Doorknob turns
                              Heart stops
Scramble out of bed
Wrinkled clothes
                    scattered
Papa emerges
Smile disappears
Rage
What is this?
Realization sinks in
Are you a faggot now?

                    Papa please I can explain
Fiery rage
Papa sees red
Fists pummel
Taste iron
Blow to the stomach
Breath knocked out
                              Blur
On the floor
Sharp toed shoe against ribs
Stop! You're hurting him!
Gunther covers me
Papa drags him by the hair
Throws him out the door

Mama kneels beside me eyes lost

Papa's words
          drip

venom
You are not my son anymore
I wash my hands of you
You've dug your own grave
Blood stained
knuckles shake

49: ARREST

Blue sweater
Chilly evening
Pen and paper keep me company
Troublesome thoughts torment

Harsh knock
Front door
Repeated rapping
Gestapo!
Aufmachen!

Mama freezes
Tea cup slips
Shattered glass
Periwinkle
Go upstairs Dieter
She rushes to the door
trembling
Two men
Short
Tall
Black trench coats
All-knowing eyes
Rudely push past her
How may I help you?
Mama asks coolly

Does Dieter Bastian Kuhn reside here?
Emotionless voice

What is it you want with him?

Short man seethes
Raises swift hand
Slaps Mama across the face

Schtill! We ask the questions

Appear at Mama's side
I am Dieter

Bring him
Short man snarls

Stomach
lurches
Heart
in my
throat
Head
spins

    I won't let you take my son!
    He's done nothing wrong
    Mama's screams cut

Papa's strong arms restrain
Heidi it's better this way
He will be reeducated

    What have you
    done? He's our
    flesh and blood!

I did what's best for him

Body
limp
One
foot
in
front
of
the

other
Shoved into a windowless van
Doors lock
Darkness
suffocates

50: TELL THEM I WAS HERE

Gestapo Headquarters
No. 8 Prinz-Albrecht- Strasse
Berlin, Germany

Gunther
I finally had the pleasure
of visiting your beautiful city
Accommodations are lacking though
No luxurious hotel room
No satin sheets
No chef's special to devour
No bubbly champagne to toast

Instead stingy captors
have given me the
cold moldy
                              isolation cell
Bed
Pile of sour straw
Beady eyed rats keep me company

Your face
                              a cruel vision
Defining light
against stone
Hands search stuffy air
Image escapes

Head throbs
Nothing left
only racing jumbled thoughts
Survival mode
Left eye swollen shut
S.S. Officer's friendly welcome

Matthew Noel

Stomach rumbles
Three days confinement
Tomorrow unknown

51: JUDGEMENT DAY

Empty Court Room   Staunch men   Self righteous   Dark
robes

Rabid wolves masquerading as vengeful gods

Frozen eyes slice through flea bitten skin
Wiry judge
Monotone
Dieter Bastian Khun
You have been accused
of violating Paragraph 175
of the German Criminal Code
Do you deny these charges?

Blank stare
Sweat
No
I do not

Your father reported
your transgressions
in hopes of saving you
There are other options
if you are willing to cooperate
This Gunther Heisenberg
did he seduce you?

No
he did not

Your father and mother say otherwise

Defiant
I seduced him

Very well then
As you know unnatural sex acts
are punishable
under the law

Matthew Noel

Pause

Exasperated sigh

Dieter Bastian Khun
you are charged with
Chronic homosexuality
Sentenced to seven months
Dachau concentration camp
Court dismissed

PART II:

The Pink Triangle

1: FATHER, FORGIVE THEM

Covered van
Bumpy road
Shoulders touch
Seven men
sentenced
same fate

Ginger bearded priest
Bloody nose
Dirt stained cassock
Clasped hands
Parched throat prays
Hail Holy Queen,
Mother of mercy...

My cracked lips form the words
Our light
Our sweetness
Our hope

Priest interrupts
Catholic?

Yes a cradle Catholic

Father Josef

Dieter

Why have they sent you here?

I'm a 175'er

Ah they're coming after all of us now

What about you?

I preached a sermon they didn't approve of

No one is safe anymore

That's why we have to stick together

Doesn't the Church condemn me just as the Nazis do?

Cast down eyes
They say the same thing about
our Jewish brothers and sisters
But they do not speak for God
You are a human being
deserving of love
Uninvited tears threaten
Gut wrenching sobs
Fr. Josef holds me close
Sings softly
Ave Maria
gratia
plena...

2: FOREIGNER IN A STRANGE LAND

Raus! Raus! Filthy schwein!
Onslaught of insults
Guards shout
No time to think
Move quickly
Don't stop or suffer blows

S.S. Officer's whip
Father Josef trips
Guard's delight
Get up Jew lover!
Closed fists strike
over
and
over
Muddy cassock
lies face down motionless
Jarring reality
Realization
of what's
to come
Ave Maria

Snarling German shepherds
Sleek coats
Foaming mouths

Open area   Graveled ground Stone
arch   Golden Eagle Swastika eyesore
Sturdy iron gates
Inscription
Arbeit macht frei

Work makes one free

Lush poplar trees line streets

Well-tended flower boxes flaunt flimsy
hyacinths slender tulips

Cleanliness gleams
Organized annihilation

Welcome to Dachau

3: FORSAKEN

Single
file
line!
Orders flung out
German
Polish
Confusion
Chaos
Guards' clubs swing
Order restored

Shunt room
Eight sturdy tables along axis
Stone pillars divide large room
First table
Papers stacked
S.S. Officer
Chiseled face
Sparkling teeth
Sandy blonde hair slicked back
Sinister deceit

Full name

Dieter Bastian Khun

Age?

17

Crime?

Paragraph 175

Ah a cocksucker

Eyes meet
Boiling anger

Eyes down pig!

Shiny
black
wooden

club
Cheekbone
Head spins
Stars
No tears
Refuse
Knees rub
concrete floor

Aufstehen!
On your feet!

Wobbly legs stand
Shock
Blood drips
Broken nose
World fractured

4: THE BLUE SWEATER

Doorway
Shoved inside
Clouded mind struggles to comprehend
Stubbled bald men
whisper life-saving advice
Keep your head down and don't
draw attention to yourself
You'll stand a better chance
this way
Haunted
Starving
Ghosts

Remove all clothing
and turn in any belongings
Someone doesn't comply
Rebellious boy
Austrian violinist
Wavy chocolate brown hair
Musician's porcelain hands
Battered violin case
Guards attack
Family heirloom
crushed underneath crossbones
Furious clubs erase life
Step over bloody pulp
Frail body twitches

Naked shame
Hands cover private parts
Shiver
Teeth chatter
Guards jeer

Unbutton blue sweater
Toss on heap of clothes
Remnants

Mama they have stolen my soul

5: POLE HANGING

                        Grimy
                    calloused
                            hands
                    grip
                        bony
                    shoulders
Clippers graze head

                    Sit still!
Slaps
issued out
Blood mingles
with clumps of hair

                Spread
                your
                legs!

Fist against cheek
Pubes shorn

                Get up!
                Schnell!

Another room
Archways
Bleached walls
Sprinklers
Freezing
murky
brown
water

trickles
Cupped hands drink thirstily
Steady stream abruptly turns off
Sticky delousing spray
S.S. Officers scan mob
Target weakest prey
Older man
stories
written
across
aged
face
Teenage
boy
ruddy
cheeks
innocence
raped
High Ceiling
Wooden beams between interior pillars
Sharp hooks

                                Hands chained
                                     Tied
                                   above
                                   heads

Bare feet
balance
on footstool
Gleeful
S.S. Officer's
swift kick
Bodies swing
                    Hang

                suspended

Matthew Noel

Screams
Wrists break
Ravenous wolves
devour spotless lambs

6: PINK TRIANGLES

Herded outside
Bare skin drenched
Rows of five
SS Officer towers
over us
Claws
        extracted
Ready to pounce
There is but one road
to freedom faggots
and that is through work!
Its milestones are
Obedience
Order
Cleanliness
And love of the Fatherland
Remember your place degenerates!
Leather horsewhip
strikes exposed flesh
Scarlett welts
Leftover scars
New clothes
Sweaty
ragged
shirt
Sleeves too long
Faded trousers too short
Scratchy cap
covers shorn shame
Mama what
would you say
if you could

Matthew Noel

see me now
Identity stolen
Truth exposed
for all to see?

7: BRANDED

Given
precious
bent
metal
shapes
and
cloth
we
are
told
to fashion
our own brands of shame:

Criminals = green

Politicals = red

Anti-Socials = black

Jehovah's Witnesses = purple

Emigrants = blue

Jews = yellow

Roma = brown/purple

Homosexuals = pink

Lowest
of the

8: BARRACKS

Menacing
machine guns
Watchtowers
Electric barbed wire
Autumn breeze
tears through clothes
Crude barracks glare

Pink Triangles
assigned special barracks
S.S. fear we'll contaminate other prisoners

Inside
Suffocating
Concrete floor
Rows of
wooden berths
Tiers of three
Rough tables
Benches
Straw sacks
Flea infested
Lice crawling
New bed
Mama you
would be
horrified
by the stench
Memories tease
Laundry day
Clean
white
sheets
Scents of lavender

waft through open window
Mama's caring smile
Lump in my throat
Find
your
bunks
queers!
Our barrack's
Blockführer
bellows

Seventeen
to eighteen
men share
one bunk

Sardines
packed
tight
Sweat
Shit
Confusion
Assault on the senses
Pressed together
Want to
claw
my
way
out
Taste
sunlight
before
it's
swallowed
up
Gunther
where are
you?

9: BARRACK'S RULES

Shiny waxed floors
Shoes must be removed before entering
Bunk is to be constructed neatly
Blanket folded
Sheet tucked tight
Failure to follow specific folding guidelines
=
Twenty-five lashes

No touching
Hands where
I can see them cocksuckers!
If you sick fucks get any
perverted ideas
I'll beat you bloody!
Alfred
Head Kapo brays

No talking

Eye contact forbidden

Toilets used only when given permission
If you have to go
too bad
Hold it
or
soil yourself

                    600 to 1,000
                    Pink Triangles
                    One barrack
                    Starving
                    Racked with disease
                    Chattel

10: FIRST NIGHT

Middle bunk
Grip edge
Barely any room
Sleep evades
Constant sounds
Coughs
Moans
Anguished cries
penetrate stillness
Milky white skeletons
pray for death
Someone leans
over
top bunk
Spews
stream
of slime
Green vomit
Specks spatter
chapped cheeks
Smelly sleeve
wipes away
brother's bile
Mama
Gunther
Gather thoughts
Drown out noises
Weary eyes close
Fleeting sensations
Village
appears
unscathed

Matthew Noel

Picture
perfect
Home
Distant memory

11: NIGHT PROWLERS

Up schwein!
Abrupt curses
Awake
Groggy
Tumble
Concrete floor
Hurry up buttfuckers!
Eight of us are chosen
Separated
Herded outside
Clothes off!
Stripped down
we run
Clubs
Oxtails
encourage
faster pace
Pitch
black
musty
room
Metallic
Iron
Execution room
Door slams shut
Oh god
Heartbeat
pounds
Constant
drum
Faces
against

the wall
perverts!
Nose
presses
cold
concrete
Tears
threaten
I will not
give them
the satisfaction
Mama I will see
you soon
Gunther
I love you
Gunshots fire
Sulfur
Wait for
sweet escape
death will bring
Deep belly laughs
interrupt trauma
Guards revel in
our shock
Get dressed idiots!
Confusion
Life spared
Why?
It's a game
the guards like
to play on
new arrivals
Shooting
volleys
into the air
Pretend

execution
Seasoned
prisoner
tells me
in hushed
tones

Mama
I
am
in
Hell

12: ZÄHLAPPELL

Anstellen!
Kapos' clubs
against wood

4:00am

Outside
Frigid morning air freezes breath
Line up in rows of five!
Arms glued to sides
        Eyes
        averted
Hours
upon
hours
Eternity
We
wait
They count us
Even the dead
Lice
    crawls
over
glacier
skin
Taste
stale
maggots

13: SPARKS

Finde das schwein!
Kapos
scramble
Search barracks frantically
Guards strike triangles
standing in front rows
Unlucky victims

Someone is missing
Lanky man beside me mumbles

                                    Willem Braam
                                    the Dutch boy
                                    I saw him sleeping
                                    behind the barracks
                                    someone whispers

S.S. Officers
Starched
forest green
uniforms
Haul frail boy
Pathetic creature
Ripped shirt hangs
Mutilated face barely recognizable
Puffy bruises

Memories interrupt
Bonfire
Heart jumps
Familiar face
Otto's lover
from the village!

Camp Kommandant
Piercing eyes
Colors of the sea
Unpredictable
Strolls
Peacock strut
You schwein think this is a rest camp!
Shiny boot
knees Willem
Guards cover head
Blood soaked
potato sack
Douse body
Gasoline
Strike match
Lapping flames engulf
Agonizing screams
penetrate choked silence
Burning human flesh stings nostrils

Willem's ashes float up
                    Cloudless sky
                 Daybreak emerges
                  Amber sparks
                   irradiates
                    horizon

14: METAMORPHOSIS

My demons take form
Reaching out through
hidden cracks
Nails against chalkboard
ring in my ears

Leaves turn to dust
Soul canvasses silence
Breaths of air
Broken feet against glass

Pavement black as coal
marrying skin and bones
Ruptured under twilight's dim
Stumbling into one's-self

Spirit detaches
circling empty vessel
Craves the light that left
Cosmos oblivion scattered

Metamorphosis changing
Cocoon ripped at the seams
Demon dying beneath the sun
From blood and ash
Angel wings

Fireflies catching stars
hold memories entombed
Moonlight chokes the dark
Twisted cross burns against flesh
Transformation

15: FEAST

Necessities are hard to come by
Never
lose
your
bowl
No
bowl
means
no
soup

Food
rations
Black
moldy
bread
Sawdust
Questionable soup contents:
Twigs
Leaves
Occasional sliver
greasy sausage
Turnips
Potato peelings
(if you're lucky)

Starvation torments dreams
Hunger claws stomach

Pray for manna

God
is
silent

Hold nose
Gulp down
rancid broth

16: AUF WIEDERSEHEN DEUTSCHLAND

Mama I see you walking through nightmares
Encampment of angels sing:

Hush child
rest your weary head
I would extinguish my light for you
I want you to glow in the night sky
not billow up in a cloud of smoke

      Bombs fall   Earth bleeds   Air chokes   Toxic fumes

Policemen
Politicians
Lawyers
Judges
Wives
Fathers
Daughters
Sons
Neighbors
Schoolmates
Old friends
You have dressed yourself
in the uniform of defeat
Skull/crossbones your armor
I am the enemy

I pray memories of ghosts behind barbed wire torment you
as you make your way home along the road of failure
back from the inferno

Do not think you will escape unscathed
We will tear apart your mind
Scream into your soul

Remind you of our strength
just as you magnified
our weaknesses

17: WORK ASSIGNMENTS

New arrivals
will be assigned
work details!
Alfred
growls

Whatever you do
try to avoid
the rock pits
Seasoned
prisoners
warn us

Assignment:
Road work
detail

We will
get to go
outside of
the camp
for work
Starry eyed
teenage boy
Toothless smile

What difference
does that make?
Bitterness coats
my sand paper tongue

Sometimes the
townspeople
sneak us food
He salivates

I'd rather starve than take their handouts

18: TOOLS

You have to be quick
if you want to get the best tool
Don't hesitate
Experienced voices echo

Get to work!
Blockführer roars

Confused herd stampedes
Adrenaline
Shove
Elbow
Fight
Weed through
metal and wood
Broken
pickaxes
Shovels
Wheelbarrows

Got one!
Victorious owner
of rusty shovel

Others aren't so lucky
Leave empty handed

Poor fellows won't last a week
Wrinkled grandfather sighs

Harsh curses thunder
Sporadic beatings rain down
Hyacinths wilt

19: PARADE OF SKELETONS

Roll call
Endless waiting
Morning routine
before road work detail
Feet blister inside wooden clogs
Storm clouds hover over
scabbed heads
Split lips thirst for rain

Road work detail
Drunken guards shout commands
Order us to sing marching songs
Step high! Sing louder swine!
Dachua's gates open
Taste freedom
Illusion
We walk on parade
Townspeople peer out from
behind lace curtains
Certainty keeps them warm

In the end
they will say they never knew
Claim they never saw us
Maybe we were invisible
Rotting flesh transparent
Zombies polluting their clean streets
Enemies of German Utopia
Easy to overlook
Easy to forget

Do not believe them

Matthew Noel

Plump woman
Lilac scarf covers wavy blonde locks
Face of Germany
Filthy scum! I hope
they finish you all off!
She spits
Shields two wide eyed children
behind A-line skirt

20: LOOSE

Who are you?

The clanging bell

Where are you going?

The inferno

Time silence your drum

Who am I?
Am I in a dream?
Will I wake up and be exactly who I thought I was before flashes
of light put stars in my eyes?
This isn't a dream anymore

In the years prior dreams were made of
tall waving grass
endless fields
dots of color
bare feet
plowed up earth

Life was a river luring me

down
      crooked paths

Stop before you say I am one dimensional
I am many wondrous things
Crinkled pages covered with fairy dust
I can fly if I want to

Anger
Me
Liar
Fraud   Stop   before you say it

If you say it glass will break
Shards are difficult to find
Where will you put the pieces shining off the floor?
I am that which is
I am here
Feet planted firmly on the ground
Looking up
Praying into thin air

Lately the gods of truth are telling lies

21: SACRIFICE

Blistered hands dig under Kapos' watchful eyes
Vultures

Fantasies interrupt
Cool water
Tongue sandpaper
Dust blurs vision
Graceful beautiful man   collapses
Guards' dogs unhinged
Kapos scream
Clubs pund
Mangy jackals
hungry for blood
Get up princess!
Alfred strikes victim with furor

Rational thought
tossed
aside
Fueled
pent
up
rage
Shield
between
assailant
and prisoner

Alfred pauses
stunned by boldness
Stubborn defiance wins
Get back to work cocksucker!
Wood against jaw

Matthew Noel

Crack
Dizzy
Throbbing pain

Worth it

22: MIKOLAJ

Long two hour trek back to camp
Dusk consumes day
Graceful man scoots close
Why would you put yourself in
danger like that for me?
He cringes with each step
Defined cheek bones bruised

I don't know what came over me

You're either insane or very kind

Probably just insane
Chuckle
I'm Mikolaj
and who are you
darling?
Dieter

We must remember our names
before the vampires steal even that from us

They'll never break me
I like your spirit!
I would like to say dziękuję bardzo

Pardon?
Oh sorry
sometimes
my polish
slips out
Thank you very much for everything

Matthew Noel

You're welcome

You now have a pezyjaciel in me
There I go again! Pezyjaciel means friend

23: QUEEN OF DACHAU

Endless night
Bunks   Huddle close   Not too close

Mikolaj squeezes in beside me
Nervous hands bleed
I grew up in a sleepy Polish town
Craved excitement
As soon as I turned eighteen
I packed a little violet satchel
and left the village to come to Berlin
I started performing at a Cabaret bar
Voice a song
Wistful gaze
I wore lavish gowns
Painted my face
Danced the nights away
Now look at me!
Queen
Heir to misery
Seated on a throne of molded straw

I've never been to a Cabaret bar

Oh honey, then you've never lived!
It was marvelous
No judgement
No shame
We lived authentically
That is until monsters raided the bar
Arrested us undesirables

Someone vomits
Another coughs up blood
Bedtime sounds

Matthew Noel

What do you miss most about Berlin?

Music   I miss music more than anything else in the world

24: LIVE

Knowing I had a friend
courage surged back into my blood
I saw a patch of sky
The sun's rays tempted me
I had forgotten light
Dachau strangled hope
but truth illuminated night
Small acts of human kindness
tore through a backdrop of violent brutality
It stoked the soul
Ignited a fire

Live! Live! Live!

25: PUPPETS

Undress! No talking!

Peel off dust coated clothes
Puss filled blisters burn palms
Terror wracks chilled body
What's going on?

Don't worry this is routine
Mikolaj reassures softly
Sharp shoulder blades protrude

Chaotic bathhouse
Crowd under open shower head
Relish cleanliness
Short lived

Out schwein!
S.S. Guards yap

Run out into frosty air
Trousers stick to soaked legs

Arrogant Senior officers stroll
Eager observers
Encouraged by prestigious audience
Blockführer puffs out chest
On the ground! Roll faggots!

Drop   Roll
Jagged gravel
Onlooking officers cackle
Entertained
Faster lazy shits!
Furious kicks
Kapos assist

Stand up!
Wet skin
Cemented dust
Scum of the earth

26: BODIES

We pass them every day on our way to Appell

Stacked
one
on
top
of
the
other

Naked
Lifeless
Grayish green
Sunken cheeks
Gaping mouths
Broken teeth bared

Glazed over eyes
beg for God

Scavengers gnaw
diseased flesh

Wooden carts
haul away ghosts

Stolen voices
ring in our ears

Our future selves on gross display
before disbelieving eyes

27: HUNGER

Winter brings
unforgiving
vengeance
Feathery
snowflakes
float
  down
Thirsty tongues catch crystals

Line up
Food rations
Clumsy fool bumps into me
Bowl drops
Precious soup leaves imprint
Snowy ground
Bastard!
Crouch on all fours
Lap up morsels
Wind bites raw cheeks

Dieter stop! I'll share mine
Mikolaj's soft voice
breaks through madness
Yanks me back

Horror

What have I become?
Spirit stands outside of the body
Crazed animal

Food
the god
I worship

Matthew Noel

Mama
I am broken

28: DROWNING

Toilets
Long line
Sea of bald heads
Familiar face hides behind pale mask

Otto is that you?
Defeated head lifts
Relief washes over

Dieter? Oh my god it's really you!
Embrace

Don't! If the Kapo sees...

Reluctant arms fall

I can't believe you're here

*Why are you here
is the better question?
I thought you were
one of them*

*I arrived yesterday
Horst that son of a bitch
found out about me and Willem
Denounced us
We planned to hide in the woods
I waited and waited but Willem never showed
Heard they arrested him
tortured him until he caved
Then they came for me*

I told you the Nazis couldn't be trusted

Matthew Noel

I know
Resignation
Otto's fiery spirit diminished

> *Do you know what happened to Gunther?*

Arrested

Stomach pangs

> *Do you know if*
> *Mama is well? Had you*
> *seen her recently?*

Apprehensive
Pursed lips
After they took
you away your
Mama was found in the river
Drowned
Suicide

World shatters
Fragile pieces
                    break
Numb

I'm so sorry Dieter
Have you seen Willem?
No one seems to know where he is
Searches my eyes
Desperate for hope
Please tell me the truth

Flashbacks
Smoke
Lapping flames
Willem's screams

S.S. Officer's laughter
I can't lie

He was set on fire

Fucking animals!
Angry fists pound wall
Son of the Fatherland crumbles

29: FLY

Misty clouds
Foggy morning
Appell
Secure spot
in the middle
instead of
the outside
Lucky for once
Decaying bodies
block biting wind
Stomp feet
Keep blood circulating
Frozen statue

Two rows down
listless Otto quakes
I offer risky smile
Hollow eyes burn into mine
He bolts from line
Frostbitten feet
Virgin white snow
Bloody footprints
Halt you!
Bewildered guards threaten
Stop! Get back in line!
Kapos surround
Otto breaks through   Hurls himself
into electric fence
Singed flesh
Smoking rags

At least he
took his own life
before the bastards could

Hunched over ghost grins
Lonely ravens caw
Shimmering wings flutter
Auf wiedersehen mein freund

30: PSALM

I scream at the sky

but the birds do not answer me

I pray to the god

who remains silent in my suffering

I search for Truth

but she has been murdered

Bald headed alien formed of stardust and earth

My Creator has abandoned me

My enemies long to dine on my weaknesses

Tear me limb from limb

Leave my rotting corpse exposed

Food fit for lowly scavengers

31: FEVER

Fetal position
Barrack's floor
Raspy cough
Chest tightens
Violent fever
Death tempts

What are you doing on the floor?
Mikolaj carries me
You're burning up!
Rolls thin body
onto bottom bunk
I'll be back

Clouded vision
Head swims
Memories carry

Home
Safe and sound
Mama comforts
My poor baby
you're running a fever
Cold cloth cools clammy forehead
She reads a rhyme
from worn copy of
<u>Max and Moritz</u>
Favorite book of mine
Young mind enthralled
by the two mischievous boys
and their silly pranks
Mama laughs along with me
Stubborn fever breaks

Matthew Noel

Dieter? Are you awake?
Mikolaj interrupts heaven
I've brought you
four aspirin
and an extra blanket

How did you get these things? It's impossible!

I have my ways darling
Now rest! I'm not letting
you leave this easily

Force smile
Thank you for everything

Think nothing of it
We are in this together comrade

Fitful sleep

32: THE VEIL

Feverish nightmares
Veiled lady
Subtle tones
Aqua blue
Scent of cloves
Fresh bread
Firewood
Nostalgia
Angelic voice
          booms across dimensions
Through tangled thoughts
Sharp images unfold
Turbulent clouds descend
Feet run in place
Stop
at cliff's edge
Pointed rocks
        below
Darkness threatens to swallow me up
Heart pounds like a drum
Lady embraces me
Whispers in my ear

I never left you

                                        Mama...

33: INSPECTION

2:00am

Anstellen!
Barrack inspection!

Scramble
Rush
Stand
at rigid
attention
S.S. Guards
check
bunks
Meticulous eyes
look for anything
out of place

Over here! Who do these belong to?
S.S. Guard shouts
Holds up
bottle of
aspirin
Pack of
cigarettes
Two musty
pieces of bread
No one
claims
precious
items
Sadistic
Alfred
turns
crimson

Club
strikes
sunken faces
Teeth   fly
Blood   spurts
Who brought these items in here?
Answer me pigs!

Mikolaj steps
forward
shaking like a leaf

I should've known it was you princess
Alfred
revels
in our
defenseless
vulnerability
Grips
Mikolaj
cruelly
by the ear
Drags
wiry
body
kicking
screaming

34: THE WHIPPING HORSE

For your thievery
and for bringing unauthorized
items into the barrack
you will be flogged
thirty times at the
whipping horse
Commandant smacks teeth
Twisted grin
Humanity shed

Mention of
the Whipping Horse
sends collective shudders
Cruel
wooden
torture
device
Restrains arms
Upper body immobile

Remove
your
clothes!

Mikolaj trembles
Clothes
fall
Fair
skin
gleams
against
winter's
piercing rays
Dachau's queen

remains
regal

35: MERCY

Angel faced S.S. Officer
Spotless
white
gloves
grasp
horsewhip
Lashes
filled
with
steel

                           Crack!

Lightning tip slices
Mikolaj's exposed bottom
Repressed screams

                           Pause

Eternity

                           Crack!

Second
strike
cuts
deeper
Third
strike
Fourth
strike
Fifth
strike

                       God! Please!

Mikolaj begs
S.S. Officer
Stone gargoyle
Unmoved

Crack!

Skin rips open
Bloody mess
Mikolaj faints
Crown stolen
Kingdom
overthrown

36: KINGDOMS FALL

Throw water on him!
Slurred speech
S.S. Officer drowns in liquor
Greedy mouth nurses vodka bottle

Freezing cold water
Mikolaj sputters
Comes back to life
Barely

What do you say schwein?
Booted foot lifts to lips

I am sorry Sir

Say it like you mean it cocksucker!

I am sorry Sir

Louder!
Whip snaps
Lash
after
lash
Screams turn to
soft weak moans
We pray for swift end

Breathless silence

Alfred checks fluttering pulse
He's alive Sir

Untie him and take him away
S.S. Officer nonchalant

Mikolaj's mutilated shell collapses
Kapos grab arms
Drag inside barrack
Scarlett stained snow

37: LULLABY

Nighttime chases memories
Winter's chill enters
barrack's thin walls
Cradle Mikolaj's head
Sticky bloody welts
You'll be fine
You're going to
pull through

          You're sweet darling
          but I don't share your
          optimism
          Winces

Is there
anything
I can do?

          Will you sing for me?
What would you
like me to sing?

          Anything
Mama's
soprano
resounds
in my head
      Brahm's Lullaby
Shaky
baritone notes
silence
noisy bunks

Sleepyhead close your eyes
I'll protect you from harm
You will wake in my arms

174

Guardian angels are near
So sleep on with no fear
Guardian angels are near
So sleep on with no fear

38: GHOSTS

Overcast morning
Mikolaj? Are you awake?
Gentle shake

Paralyzing anxiety

Mikolaj?
Stiff
body
topples
onto
floor
Feeble arms
encircle
willowy
waist
Tug
Pull

Mikolaj you have to get up! Why won't you wake up?

Leave him!
Kapo strikes head

Appell
Bitter cold
Death cart creaks by
Mikolaj's haunting eyes peer out
from underneath heap of bodies

No
royal
procession
Glorious queen

tossed into
mass grave

39: GERMANY, TURN AROUND

Mama floats in my dreams
Pray Dieter
Remember to pray

To whom?

Who is God?
I do not recognize His face
Rumors say She suffocated in the gas chambers with the children

No
I cannot pray

Germany
why are sleeping?
Do you hear me through the veil?
Maybe if I scream loud enough
I can prevent what will be

Germany wake up!
Wake the fuck up!

Creator
please rewrite the past
Fearsome wolves
scavenge the low lands
Blood stained mouths devour souls

Mama
pray for us

40: SNOW

Face against biting wind
Pray
skeletal
frame
will be
swept away
Carried off into a million pieces

Road work detail
Mind jumbled
Jigsaw pieces
Missing parts
No
one
to live
for anymore
Move it queers!
Alfred exhales ice
We
clear
snow
using
cracked
bleeding
bare
hands
Senseless work
S.S. officers
Fur trimmed coats
Liquor laced breath
Heavy boots grind
brittle bones into flakes

Matthew Noel

Gunther
if I had paper
I would write a thousand poems to bring us back to life

41: ANXIETY

I wake up with stone cold corpses
wrapped around my legs

Hopeless fury strangles peace in the quiet night

Illuminated stars evaporate

Violent storms hover
Starving wolves nip at shins
Ghostly ladies prophecy

Majestic snow capped mountains
Lush forest trails
Memories stored in the corners of my mind
Trove guarded by demons with swords
Glass edges against volcanic rock
Reflection staring back
Sunken hungry eyes
Frostbitten cheeks
Rotting teeth
Image erased

42: BREAD

Exhausted skeletons trudge back to camp
S.S. guard shadows me
Hazel eyes
Flecks of green and blue
Rosy red cheeks
Half lit cigarette between lips
Face holds youth imprisoned
I try to see his soul

Who was he before?
Who was I?
How are we the same?

He offers brief smile
Look away
Eyes down
Sneak peek
He smiles again
Glances around nervously
Arm outstretched
Open palm
Half loaf
Homemade bread
Real bread
Not sawdust

Here take this
Gentle voice
Stunned
Is this a cruel joke? Entrapment?
Please take it
Grab heavenly morsel

Tuck away
Save for later

Danke
Words forced
Desperate eyes ask why

Bitte schön
He gives no explanation
Tender grin offers warmth
Heart freezes

43: WALLOW

Sip turnip soup
Gulp
down
acorn coffee
Attention!
Alfred
enters
barrack
Head held high
Prince of hellish domain
You you and you come with me
He singles me out
Led adjacent room
Overflowing toilets
Clean this disgusting filth

How? With what?
Outspoken teenage Roma boy
Right hand missing four fingers from frostbite

Alfred issues abrupt blow
With your hands faggot!
Down on raw knees
Elbows deep
Festered
blistered
hands scrub dirty rims
Hold back vomit
Foul putrid chokes

Rub it on your faces little piggies
Burly S.S. guard mocks

Gun aimed

Hours later we emerge
displaying
shit stained faces

Today
I pray
for death
No regrets

44: PETER

Snow kissed cheeks
Wool scarves
Giggling children
run past our parade
through town
Road work
One tingling foot
in front of the other
Snow piled knee high
S.S. guard
Hazel eyes
Smells of pine musk
I'm Peter
Cautious compassion
Quicken pace
Distrust
Please
I didn't mean to scare you
I just figured we could
have a conversation

   Don't you know we can't speak to each other?

I don't mind breaking the rules
Inviting smile
Twinkle
    You're going to get us both killed
     Beads of sweat
What's your name?
     Painful pause
     Careful response
     I have no name

I have nothing
Thanks to you
and your Führer
Unafraid
Stare death in the face

He turns his back
Avoids flagrant truth

45: TYPHUS

Piss soaked bunk
Debilitated
stranger
coughs
Feverish body
radiates heat
Typhus
spreads
through
our barrack
S.S. are
afraid to
enter
Alfred
avoids us
like the plague
Painful
red rash
appears
on my chest
Scorching fever
Delirious stupor

Barrack mates   shove
                                                 infected
                                                triangles
                                          to far corner
                        Sour bunk by drafty entrance
                                   Worst place to be

Keep away!
You'll get the whole
barrack sick

Five of us
huddle close
Winter's shrill
wind cuts to the bone

46: FADE TO PINK

Carry snow
Hands throb
Needles
Deep cough
Fever clouds vision
Queasy stomach churns
Mind numbing confusion
Unsteady knees bend
Get up! Keep working!
Overcast fog

When did I fall?
Legs do not respond
Don't make me move

Please
I'm warm here living in the shadows of my mind
Mama can you hear me now?
I think I see you
Cup of steaming soup cradled
between elegant hands

Move!
Booted tip cracks ribs
Vast sky spins

Gunther? Are you there?
I thought the light would be brighter
Why are my eyes sinking into my sockets?

Get up!
Peter
Hazel eyes aflame
Towers over me

I am only dreaming

Kill the cocksucker!
Predators fight over carcass
Metal presses throbbing temple
Abrupt gunshot reverberates

Time lapses

                    Pink Triangles

                              haunt

                                   memory

47: MEMORIAM

Twilight breaks
Smoky gray horizon dissipates

Inhale cosmos

Universe murmurs forgotten stories
Blusterous wind
                    carries purloined voice
                                    across centuries
Caged wings expand

Goldcrest flies free singing

Never forget
Never forget
Never forget
Never forget
Never forget

HISTORICAL NOTE

On May 6, 1933 in Berlin, Germany around one hundred Nazi Brownshirts stormed the Institute for Sexual Science. They destroyed everything the could find and emptied the entire library onto the streets. Four days later a huge bonfire was built to consume the twelve thousand "un-German" books and documents. An energized crowd gathered and screamed their approval. They had been fed the political propaganda that the Institute was a "breeding ground of dirt and filth".

The institute was founded in 1919 by Dr. Magnus Hirschfield, a well known homosexual. Dr. Hirschfield was a pioneer in sponsoring research on sexuality, sexually transmitted diseases, abortion, marital issues, and homosexuality. He fought tirelessly to change laws criminalizing homosexuality.

One year later the Nazis created a special Gestapo division on homosexuals. Their first order of business was to seize the "pink lists" that German police had been systemizing since 1900. The lists contained the names of suspected homosexual men. Gay bars were raided and gay rights organizations were banned.

On September 1, 1935 the government revised Paragraph 175 of the Criminal Code, which had been in place since 1871. The revised version included ruthless punishment for lewd and lascivious behavior between men.

Heinrich Himmler, leader of the Protection Squadron; S.S., and leading member of the Nazi Party of Germany, formed a Reich Central Office of Combating of Homosexuality and Abortion. He hoped by eradicating homosexuals that it would ensure a higher birthrate for Germany's Aryan population. According to Himmler, homosexuals posed a dangerous threat and would bring about "the end of Germany and the end of the Germanic world".

Between the years 1937-1939 the persecution and prosecutions of homosexual men grew more intense. The Gestapo raided homosexual meeting places, took address books of arrested men to weed out other victims, and put together lists of names to give to informers. Often times the accused would be brought before a court of Nazi jurists and judges, unfairly tried, sentenced to time in prison, and afterwards time in a concentration camp. If the man was accused of seducing another man his sentence was much harsher. The seduced was usually castrated by force "for the good of the Fatherland".

According to historical researchers there were 1.2 million homosexual men in Germany in the year 1928. From 1933-1945, it is estimated that over 100,000 men were arrested under Paragraph 175. It is believed that over 50,000 defined homosexuals were tried and sentenced. Out of the 100,000 men, documents show that 5,000 to 15,000 were sentenced to time in concentration camps. Unfortunately, due to limited historical research it is unknown how many men were murdered in the concentration camps. Rüdiger Lautmann, a prominent German LGBTQ scholar, states that the death rate of homosexuals in the camps was probably as high as 60%.

Homosexuals were subjected to cruel torture and baseless medical experiments, such as testosterone injections. Forced castration was also a common form of punishment.

When the war ended liberation did not come for prisoners incarcerated for homosexuality. Under the Allied Military Government of Germany, many homosexuals were forced to finish out their prison terms even though they had spent time in concentration camps. Homosexual concentration camp prisoners were not recognized as victims. They were denied any reparations.

Heinrich Himmler's revision of Paragraph 175 remained

in effect in West Germany until 1969. Homosexuals still continued to live in constant fear of arrest and imprisonment. Society's homophobia and intolerance prevented homosexual survivors from coming forward and sharing their stories. Over the years, however, some survivors have spoken out about their experiences ensuring that the next generation never forgets the atrocities of the Shoah and all of its forgotten victims.

Paragraph 175:

175. A male who commits lewd and lascivious acts with another male or permits himself to be so abused for lewd and lascivious acts, shall be punished by imprisonment. In a case of a participant under 21 years of age at the time of the commission of the act, the court may, in especially slight cases, refrain from punishment.

175a. Confinement in a penitentiary not to exceed ten years and, under extenuating circumstances, imprisonment for not less than three months shall be imposed:

1. Upon a male who, with force or with threat of imminent danger to life and limb, compels another male to commit lewd and lascivious acts with him or compels the other party to submit

to abuse for lewd and lascivious acts;

2. Upon a male who, by abuse of a relationship of dependence upon him, in consequence of service, employment, or subordination, induces another male to commit lewd and lascivious acts with him or to submit to being abused for such, acts;

3. Upon a male who being over 21 years of age induces another male under 21 years of age to commit lewd and lascivious acts with him or to submit to being abused for such acts;

4. Upon a male who professionally engages in lewd and lascivious acts with other men, or submits to such abuse by other men, or offers himself for lewd and lascivious acts with other men.

175b. Lewd and lascivious acts contrary to nature between human beings and animals shall be punished by imprisonment; loss of civil rights may also be imposed.

English translation by Warren Johannson and William Perry in "Homosexuals in Nazi Germany," Simon Wiesenthal Center Annual, Vol. 7 (1990).

AUTHOR'S NOTE

Paragraph 175 is just one example of what can happen when hatred and intolerance are used by a political platform to target minorities. Throughout the world LGBTQ people are facing persecution, intolerance, and death. Same-sex relationships and sexual activities are illegal in 72 countries. In 8 countries it is punishable by death.

Uganda is one of the 36 countries in Africa where homosexuality is a crime. Its government passed the "Anti-Homosexuality Act", allowing the arrest, imprisonment, and murder of LGBTQ people. Many are denied basic necessities such as medicine or food. Upon arrest, the men are taken to a physician where an 'anal examine' is performed, a painful cruel form of torture which sometimes ends in death. According to researchers at the Human Rights Watch the hostility towards homosexuals is growing more every day.

In 2017 the government of The Russian Republic of Chechnya started an aggressive brutal attack on gays. Over 100 gay men were arrested, tortured, beaten, and detained. Human Rights organizations and credible sources from the region say that in January 2019 another purge took place. More than 40 gay men and women were detained in a makeshift prison. Two gay men were killed during the roundup. Other survivors reported being raped with police nightsticks and tortured with electrical shocks until they confessed the names of their partners and friends.

Indonesia 2017: Two gay men caught in bed together were brought before a court and sentenced to 85 lashes in a public display of punishment pertaining to Sharia Law. A few years earlier two teenage girls were seen embracing. They were accused of being lesbians, arrested, and brought before a court that issued a similar punishment.

Conversion therapy, the pseudoscientific practice of trying to change an individual's sexual orientation from homosexual or bisexual to heterosexual using psychological or spiritual interventions, is still legal in America in 36 states.

Reports from 2018 reveal that almost 3,000 transgender people were murdered in the past decade worldwide. Most were shot, stabbed, and beaten to death.

ACKNOWLEDGMENTS

This book would not have been possible without the generous help of many others.

I would like to say danke schön to Alice Goldstein for welcoming me into her life, sharing her holocaust story with me, and reading through every single draft. Her encouragement kept me going. Her contributions and personal insight were invaluable.

Thank you to John Rosenberg who took the time out of his busy schedule to share his family's story of survival under the Nazi regime with me and for assisting with the historical research. He is a true inspiration.

To Jay McCoy, my editor, who taught me a great deal about writing and pushed me out of my comfort zone. His knowledge of World War II history and passion for telling authentic queer stories inspired me to write from the heart. Thank you for helping me find my voice.

Special thanks to Sylvia Ahrens, my editor. Her fresh perspective and editing skills gave me the extra boost that I needed.

To Lisa and Trinity at the Holocaust and Humanity Center for their expertise regarding homosexuals during the Holocaust.

Grateful to Rabbi Moshe Smolkin for his spiritual input and for answering the deeper questions.

To the LGBT survivors, past and present, for being brave enough to share their stories. They are an inspiration.

And last but definitely not least, to my husband, Mac for his constant support and encouragement.

ABOUT THE AUTHOR

Matthew Noel is thirty years old and a Kentucky native. He has been an avid reader of World War II history and of the holocaust since he was a child. The idea for his story about Paragraph 175 came after researching the atrocities inflicted upon the LGBTQ community under the Third Reich. He hopes this story will shed light on the forgotten stories of queer people during World War II.

Find the author on Twitter:
http:/www.twitter.com/matthew89n

On Instagram:
@matthewn2989

Made in the USA
Monee, IL
14 January 2024

51769400R00118